The Joy of 90s Pop

Arranged by Stephen Duro.

Yorktown Music Press / Music Sales Limited
London / New York / Paris / Sydney / Copenhagen / Madrid / Tokyo

Exclusive Distributors:
Music Sales Limited
8/9 Frith Street, London W1D 3JB, England.
Music Sales Pty Limited
120 Rothschild Avenue, Rosebery, NSW 2018, Australia.

Order No. AM963270
ISBN 0-7119-8087-X
This book © Copyright 2000 by Yorktown Music Press / Music Sales Limited

Compiled by Nick Crispin.
Cover illustration by Rowan Barnes-Murphy.
Music arranged by Stephen Duro.
Music processed by Allegro Reproductions.

Music Sales' complete catalogue describes thousands of titles and
is available in full colour sections by subject, direct from Music Sales Limited.
Please state your areas of interest and send a cheque/postal order for £1.50 for postage to:
Music Sales Limited, Newmarket Road, Bury St. Edmunds, Suffolk IP33 3YB.

Your Guarantee of Quality:
As publishers, we strive to produce every book to the highest commercial standards.
The music has been freshly engraved and the book has been carefully designed to minimise
awkward page turns and to make playing from it a real pleasure.
Particular care has been given to specifying acid-free, neutral-sized paper made from
pulps which have not been elemental chlorine bleached.
This pulp is from farmed sustainable forests and was produced with special regard for the environment.
Throughout, the printing and binding have been planned to ensure a sturdy,
attractive publication which should give years of enjoyment.
If your copy fails to meet our high standards, please inform us and we will gladly replace it.

Printed in the United Kingdom by
Caligraving Limited, Thetford, Norfolk.

www.musicsales.com

Always (Bon Jovi) 4
...Baby One More Time (Britney Spears) 14
Common People (Pulp) 9
Don't Look Back In Anger (Oasis) 18
I'd Do Anything For Love... (Meatloaf) 22
Lovefool (The Cardigans) 44
No Matter What (Boyzone) 28
Perfect Moment (Martine McCutcheon) 32
Runaway (The Corrs) 36
Say You'll Be There (Spice Girls) 40
She's The One (Robbie Williams) 47
When You Say Nothing At All (Ronan Keating) 60
You Are Not Alone (Michael Jackson) 52
You're Still The One (Shania Twain) 56

Always

Words & Music by Jon Bon Jovi

pay to say these words to you.

ain't no luck in these load – ed dice but ba – by if you give me just one more try we can

pack up our old dreams and our old lives, we'll find a place where the sun still shines, yeah.——

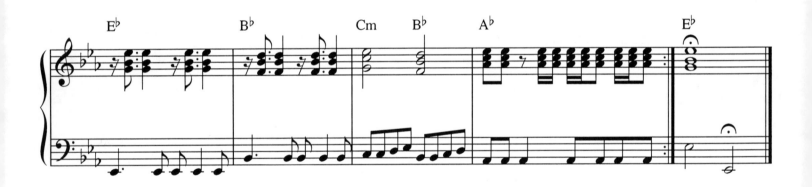

Verse 2:

Now your pictures that you left behind
Are just memories of a different life
Some that made us laugh, some that made us cry
One that made you have to say goodbye.

What I'd give to run my fingers through your hair
To touch your lips, to hold you near
When you say your prayers, try to understand,
I've made mistakes, I'm just a man.

When he holds you close, when he pulls you near
When he says the words you've been needing to hear
I'll wish I was him, 'cause those words are mine
To say to you 'til the end of time.

I will love you *etc.*

Common People

Words by Jarvis Cocker
Music by Pulp

Moderately bright ♩ = 152

She came from Greece, she had a thirst for know-ledge,
(Verse 2 see block lyric)
she stud-ied sculp-ture at St.

Mar-tin's col-lege that's where I___ caught her eye.__

___ She told me that her

but still you'll nev - er get it right. 'Cause when you're laid

in bed at night watch-ing roach - es climb the wall,

if you called your dad he could stop it all yeah.

You'll nev - er live like com-mon peo - ple, you'll nev - er do what - ev - er com - mon peo-ple

do. You'll nev - er fail like com-mon peo - ple, you'll nev - er watch your life slide out of view,

and then dance___ and drink and screw be-cause there's

noth-ing else_ to do.___

To Coda ⊕ 1. 2. *D.S. al Coda*

⊕ CODA C *Repeat ad lib.*

Want to live like com-mon peo - ple like you.

Verse 2:

I took her to a supermarket,
I don't know why
But I had to start it somewhere
So it started there.
I said pretend you've got no money
She just laughed and said oh you're so funny.
I said yeah?
Well I can't see anyone else smiling in here.
Are you sure you want to live like common people?
You want to see whatever common people see,
You want to sleep with common people,
You want to sleep with common people like me?
But she didn't understand;
She just smiled and held my hand.

13

...Baby One More Time

Words & Music by Max Martin

Oh ba - by, ba - by how was I sup - posed to know?

Oh pret - ty ba - by I should - n't have let you go.

I must con - fess that my lone - li - ness

is kill - in' me now, don't you know I still be - lieve

that you will be here and give me a sign. Hit me ba - by one more time.

Verse 2:

Oh baby, baby
The reason I breathe is you
Boy you got me blinded.
Oh pretty baby
There's nothing that I wouldn't do
It's not the way I planned it.

Show me how you want it to be   *etc.*

Don't Look Back In Anger

Words & Music by Noel Gallagher

20

Verse 2:

Take me to the place where you go
Where nobody knows if it's night or day
Please don't put your life in the hands
Of a rock 'n' roll band who'll throw it all away.

I'm gonna start a revolution from my head
'Cause you said the brains I had went to my head
Step outside, the summertime's in bloom
Stand up beside the fireplace, take that look from off your face
'Cause you ain't never gonna burn my heart out.

So Sally can wait *etc.*

I'd Do Anything For Love
(But I Won't Do That)

Words & Music by Jim Steinman

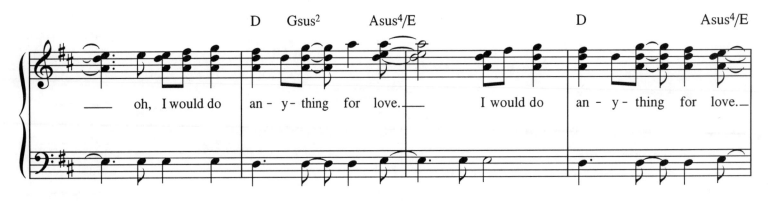

24

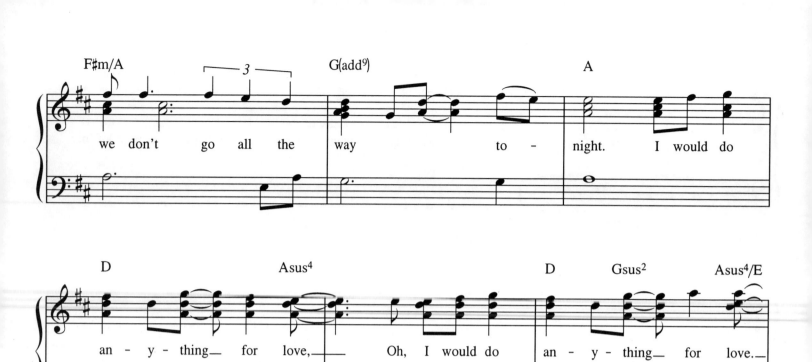

we don't go all the way to - night. I would do

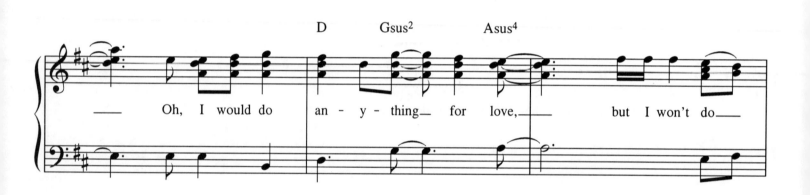

an - y - thing_ for love,_ Oh, I would do an - y - thing_ for love._

_ Oh, I would do an - y - thing_ for love,_ but I won't do_

that, no, no, no, I won't do... I would_ do an - y - thing_ for love,_

_ an - y - thing you've_ been dream - ing of, but I_ just

No Matter What

Music by Andrew Lloyd Webber
Lyrics by Jim Steinman

Moderately

teach us, what we be - lieve is true.

No mat - ter what they call us, how - ev - er they at -

- tack, no mat - ter where they take us,

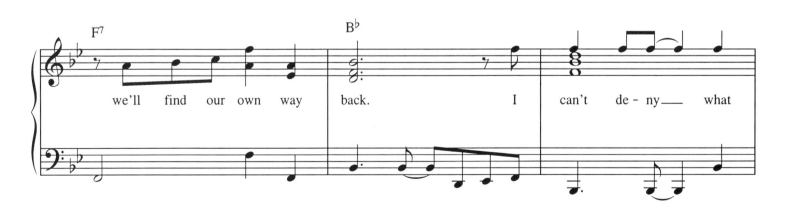

we'll find our own way back. I can't de - ny___ what

I be - lieve,— I can't be— what I'm not.—

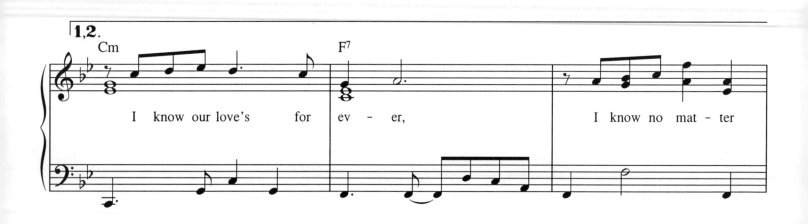

1,2.

I know our love's for ev - er, I know no mat - ter

3.

what. I know this love's for ev - er, That's all that

mat - ters now no mat - ter what. I know no mat - ter

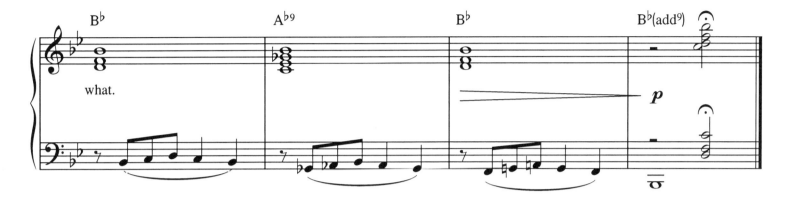

what.

Verse 2:

If only tears were laughter,
If only night was day,
If only prayers were answered
Then we would hear God say.
No matter what they tell us,
No matter what they do,
No matter what they teach you,
What you believe is true.
And I will keep you safe and strong
And sheltered from the storm.
No matter where it's barren
Our dream is being born.

Verse 3:
Instrumental:

No matter if the sun don't shine,
Or if the skies are blue.
No matter what the ending,
My life began with you.
I can't deny what I believe,
I can't be what I'm not.
I know this love's for ever,
That's all that matters now no matter what.

Perfect Moment

Words & Music by James Marr & Wendy Page

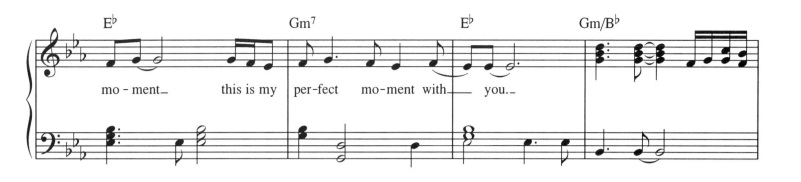

mo - ment__ this is my per-fect mo-ment with__ you.__

2. Tell me you love me when you__ leave. You're more than a sha-dow,

that's what I____ be-lieve. You take me to pla-ces I nev-er thought I'd see.____

Min-ute by min-ute you're the world to me.__ I wish I could frame____ the look in your

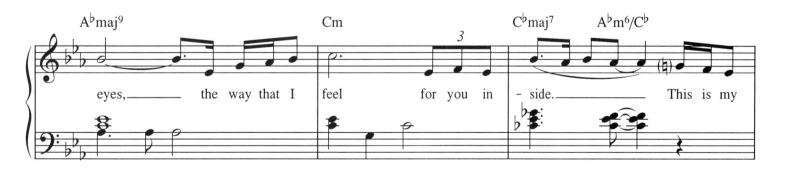

eyes,____ the way that I feel for you in - side.____ This is my

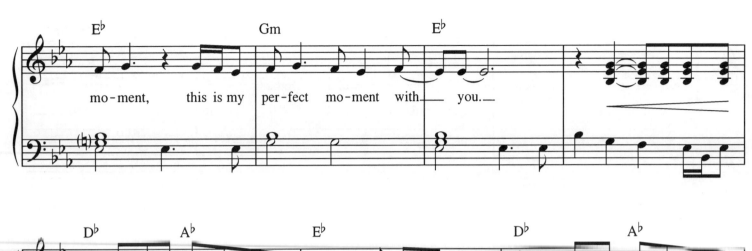

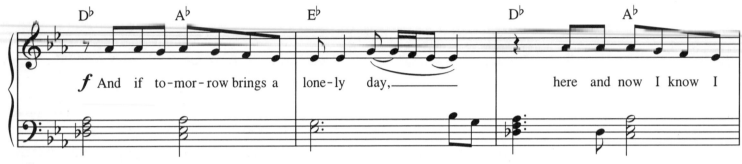

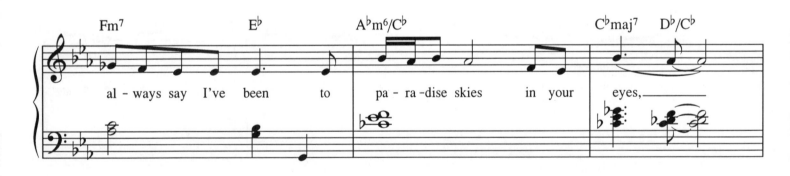

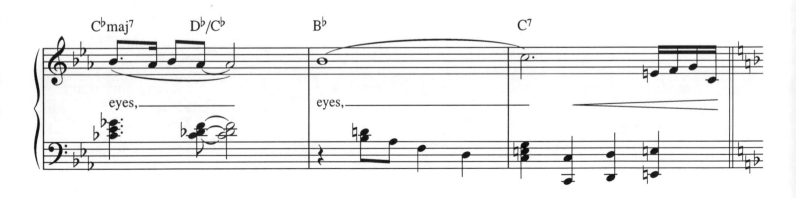

34

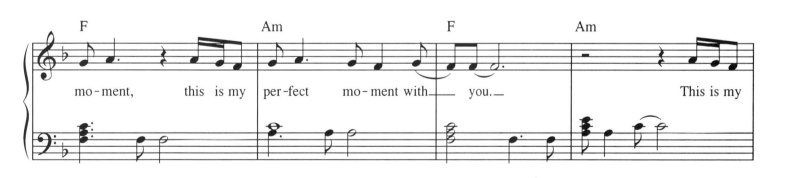

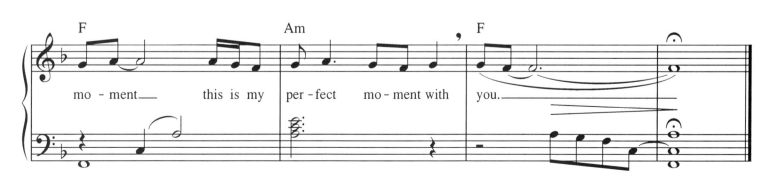

Runaway

Words & Music by Andrea Corr, Caroline Corr, Sharon Corr & Jim Corr

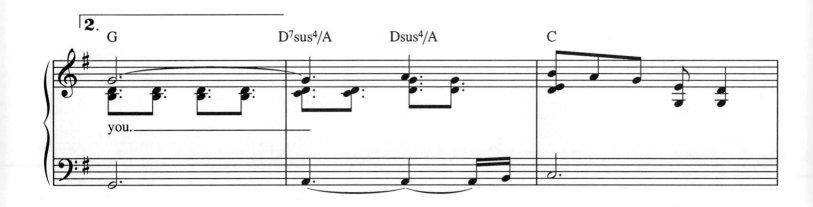

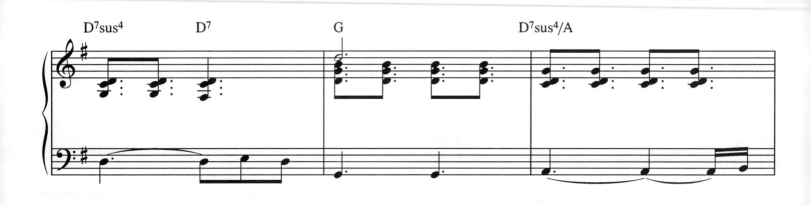

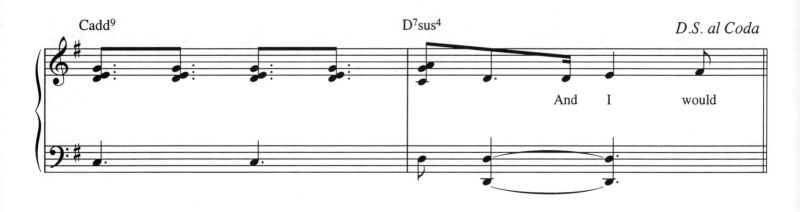

CODA

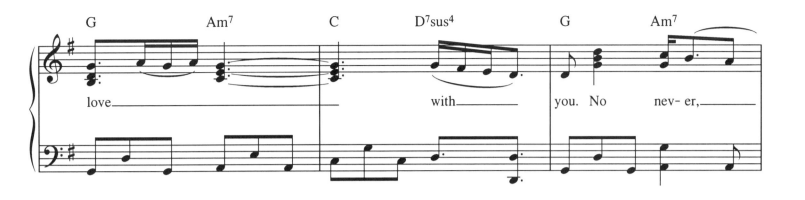

love_____ with_____ you. No nev- er,_____

_____ I'm nev - er gon - na stop fall - ing in love with

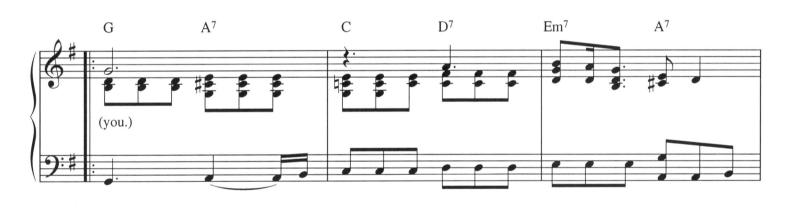

(you.)

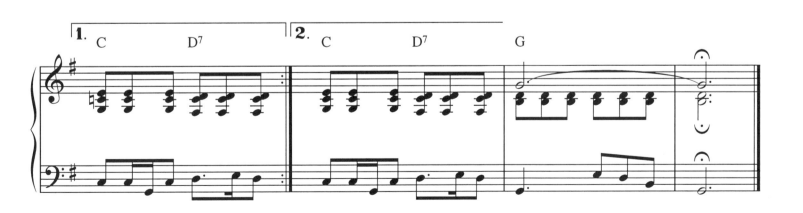

Say You'll Be There

Words & Music by Eliot Kennedy, Jon B, Victoria Aadams, Melanie Brown,
Emma Bunton, Melanie Chisholm & Geri Halliwell

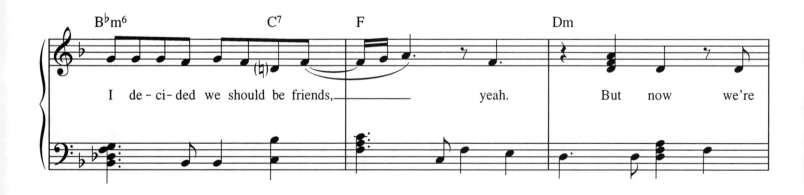

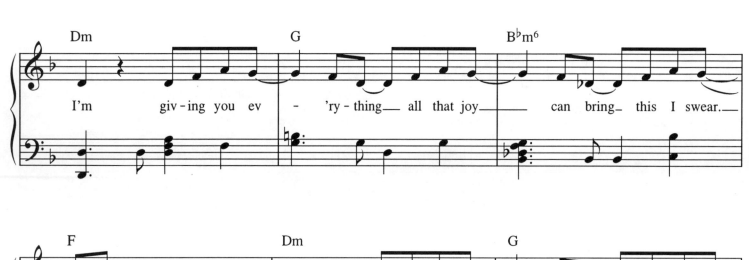

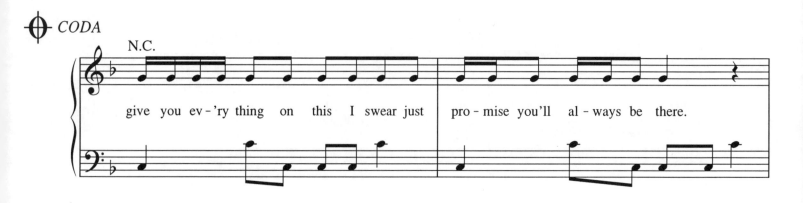

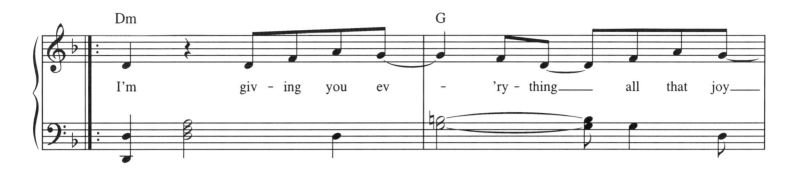

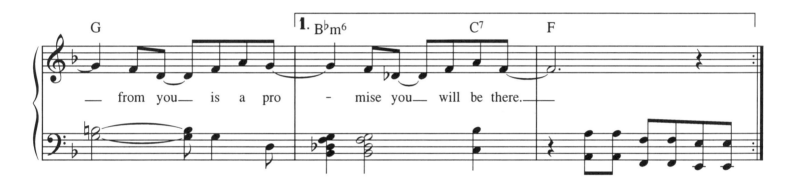

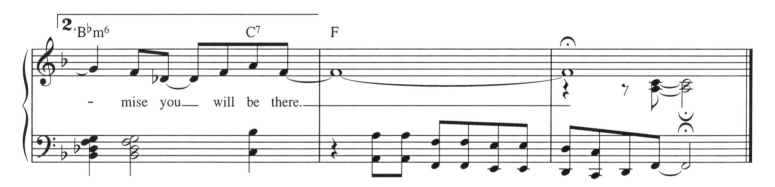

Verse 2:

If you put two and two together you will see what our friendship is for,
If you can't work this equation then I guess I'll have to show you the door.
There is no need to say you love me it would be better left unsaid.

I'm giving you everything all that joy can bring this I swear,
And all that I want from you is a promise you will be there,
Yeah I want you.

Verse 3: (Instrumental)
Any fool can see they're falling, gotta make you understand.

Lovefool

Words & Music by Peter Svensson & Nina Persson

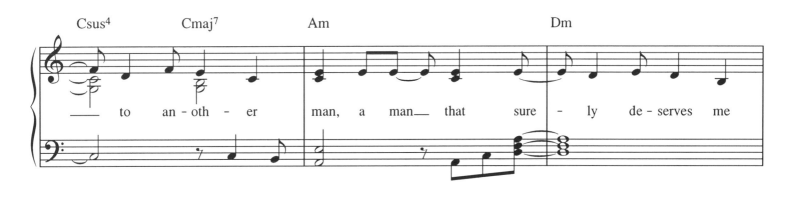

Verse 2:

Lately I have desperately pondered
Spent my nights awake and I wonder
What I could have done in another way
To make you stay.

Reason will not reach a solution
I will end up lost in confusion
I don't care if you really care
As long as you don't go.

She's The One

Words & Music by Karl Wallinger

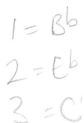

1. I was her, _____ she was me, _____ will be strong _____

(Verse 3 see block lyric)

we were one, _____ we were free. And if there's some-bo-
I know we'll _____ car-ry on, _____ 'cos if there's some-bo-

-dy call-ing me on, _____ she's the one. _____
-dy call-ing me on, _____

To Coda

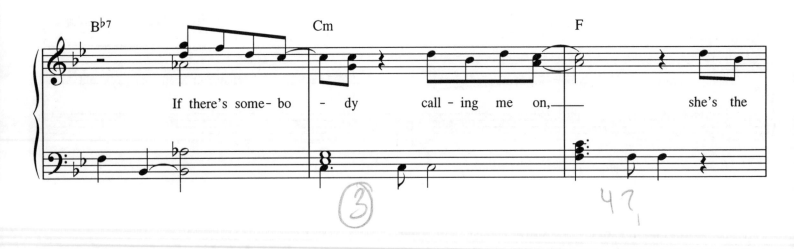

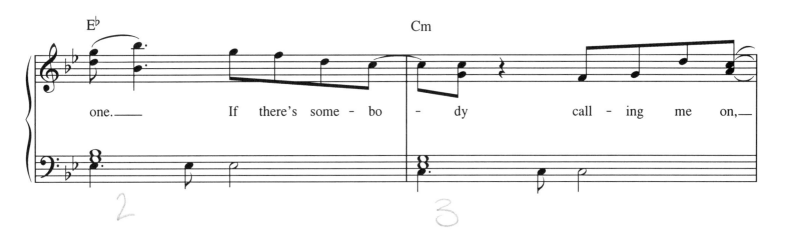

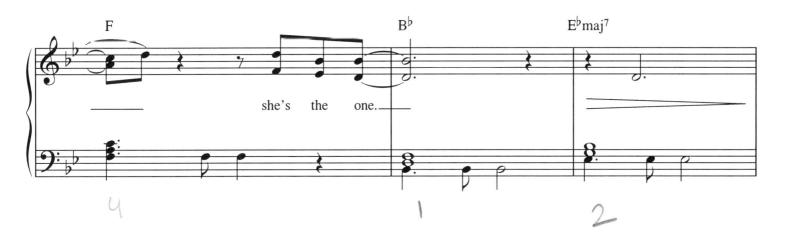

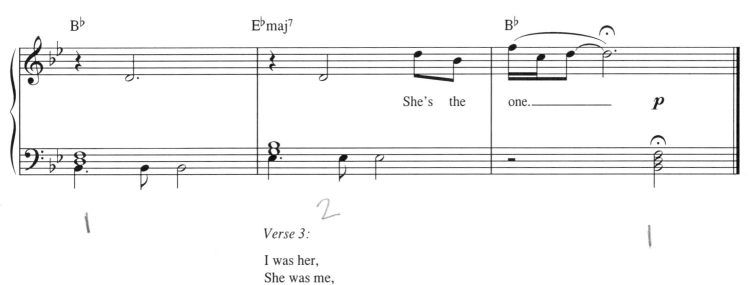

Verse 3:

I was her,
She was me,
We were one,
We were free,
And if there's somebody calling me on,
She's the one.

You Are Not Alone

Words & Music by Robert Kelly

(Spoken) You are not alone...
You just reach out for me girl
Together ...

in the morning in the

you are not alone
evening not alone...not alone...

not alone
you and me, not alone

Repeat to fade

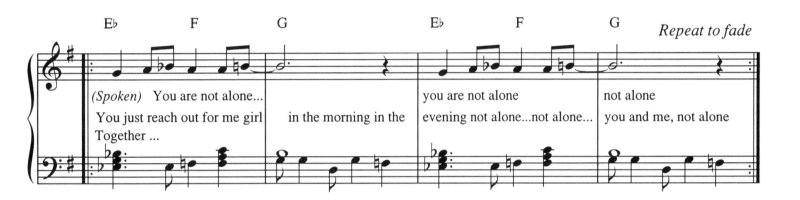

Verse 1:

You are not alone
I am here with you
Though you're far away
I am here to stay.
You are not alone
I am here with you
Though we're far apart
You're always in my heart
But you are not alone.

Verse 2:

Just the other night
I thought I heard you cry
Asking me to go
And hold you in my arms.
I can hear your breaths
Your burdens I will bear
But first I need you here
Then forever can begin.

Verse 3:

You are not alone
I am here with you
Though you're far away
I am here to stay.
But you are not alone
But I am here with you
Though we're far apart
You're always in my heart.
But you are not alone.

You're Still The One

Words & Music by Shania Twain & R.J. Lange

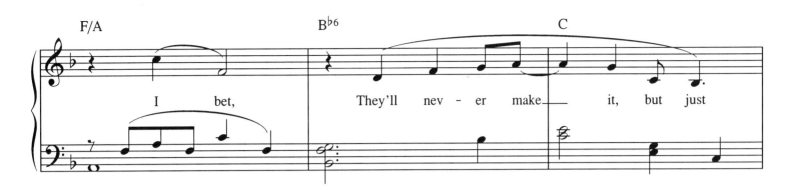

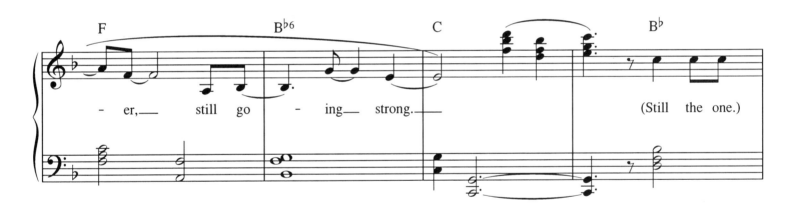

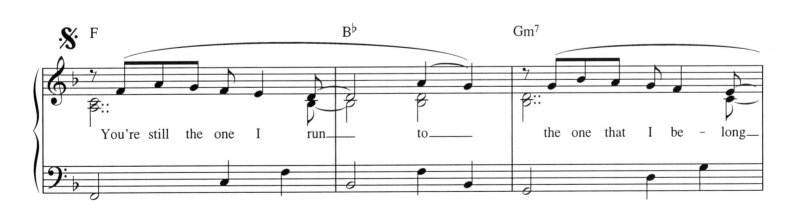

to.___ You're still the one I want___ for

life. (Still the one.) You're still the one that I___ love,___

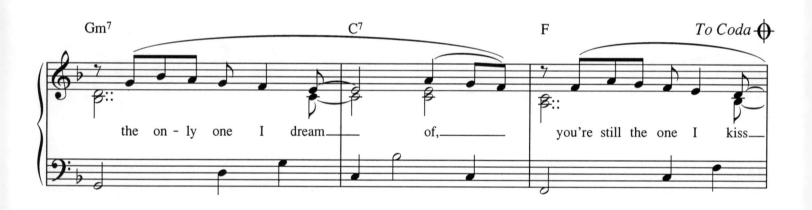

the on-ly one I dream___ of,___ you're still the one I kiss___

To Coda ⊕

___ good - night. **1.** **2.** N.C.

You're still___ the one.

D.S. al Coda

CODA

good - night._____ I'm so glad we

made it, look how far____ we've come my ba - by.

rit.

Verse 2:

Ain't nothin' better
We beat the odds together
I'm glad we didn't listen
Look at what we would be missing.

They said, I bet,
They'll never make it
But just look at us holding on
We're still together, still going strong.

When You Say Nothing At All

Words & Music by Paul Overstreet & Don Schlitz

(You say it best___ when you say___ no - thing at all.___)

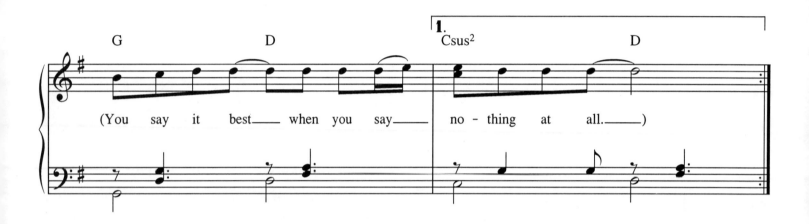

1.

(You say it best___ when you say___ no - thing at all.___)

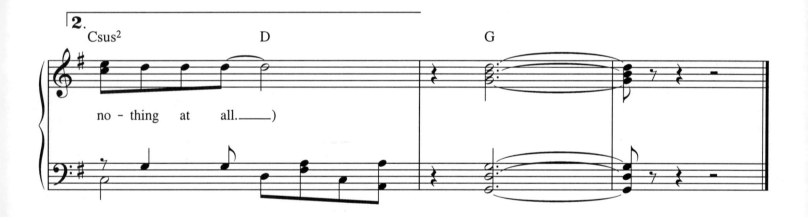

2.

no - thing at all.___)

Verse 2:

All day long I can hear people talking out loud
But when you hold me you drown out the crowd
Try as they may they can never defy
What's been said between your heart and mine.

The smile on your face *etc.*